The Bitty Twins' Tea Party

Written by Barbara Walsh
Illustrated by Stephanie Roth

What should we do today for fun?

Let's have a tea party for everyone.

It's a fancy party, so every guest will want to look her very best.

Let's help get
the table ready.

This vase of flowers will look pretty!

We'll sit together, you and me,
and be as polite as we can be.

I hope our manners are all right.
Do we know how to be polite?

Sure we do! Why, it's a breeze.

Just remember to say "Please" when you'd like something passed to you. And when you get it, say "Thank you."

I bet those cookies taste just great.
I wish they *all* were on *my* plate!

But let's make sure we each get some.
It's polite to share with everyone!

When we eat our favorite foods,
we sometimes gulp too much to chew.

Take little bites—that's better manners
when eating cookies or bananas.

We try our hardest not to spill,
but now and then we probably will.

We help Mommy clean it up.

May I please have more in my cup?

Sometimes when we're all done eating,
it's hard to stay politely sitting.

We feel all wiggly right down to our shoes.
So we ask, "May we please be excused?"

Before we both run off to play,
we think of one more thing to say:

"Thanks for coming to our party today!"

Dear Parents . . .

Your toddler is growing up! As she gets older, she's learning that mealtimes aren't just for physical nourishment—they're also a time for people to get together, share, and enjoy being together.

Teaching your little one how to make mealtime a pleasant experience will give her an important social skill as she begins to be a part of the wider world.

Invite Your Little One to Help

Give your daughter some simple tasks to help prepare the table. Show her how to set the table, and then let her try part of it herself, such as putting a spoon next to each plate.

Let her make some decisions—for example, "Should we use the red napkins or the blue ones?" Ask her for ideas for decorating the table. By taking the time to make the table look special, you're showing her that mealtime is an event to look forward to.

Keep It Positive!

Do what you can to make mealtimes cheerful and relaxed. Instead of reading or watching TV, keep the focus on each other.

The old-fashioned rule that "you can't leave the table until you've cleaned your plate" can cause tension and may escalate into an all-out battle of wills. Start with small servings, and as long as she eats a reasonable amount of several items, let her decide when she's had enough.

When there's a spill, don't be angry with your toddler. Learning to handle cups, bowls, and utensils isn't easy for little hands! Give her a wet cloth just like yours, and wipe up the mess together.

Toddlers Love to Imitate

Family members can set good examples by always saying "please," "thank you," and "excuse me" to one another. If your child sees family members treating others with generosity, kindness, and respect, she'll soon make that part of her routine, too.

All Done!

Most toddlers don't have the patience to sit still for very long—for young toddlers, five minutes at the table can be the limit. Eventually your child will develop the ability to sit for a while longer. Praise your little one when she's politely sitting and eating. When she gets restless, let her leave the table to play quietly while everyone else finishes the meal.

Keep Your Expectations Realistic

With toddlers, some days are more difficult than others. Parents don't always have the time or energy to plan a nice family meal. Toddlers may go through phases of being extremely uncooperative or picky, or "forgetting" how to feed themselves. Don't be discouraged! Be patient with your little one, and be generous with your praise when you see her following your good examples.